A DRAGON IN
THE FIRE

AND OTHER RHYMES

LAURA MERRILL

ISBN 978-2-8399-3371-1 (paperback)

Cover design and layout: Sadie Butterworth-Jones

Tales, poems, rhymes and stories for Vivi, Ruvirai, Hewie, Tilda, Nora and Ana.

A big thank you to Richard, Ella and Peter, and to Gill, who loved storytime.

Contents

A Lion, Lying In

I'm a lion lying in,
An armadillo with a pillow,
An orangutan who's a big sleep fan,
I'm a snake who doesn't wake,
A hedgehog on the nod,
A hyena who's a dreamer,
Or a llama in pyjamas,
But most of all I'm me,
Who is quite sleepy.

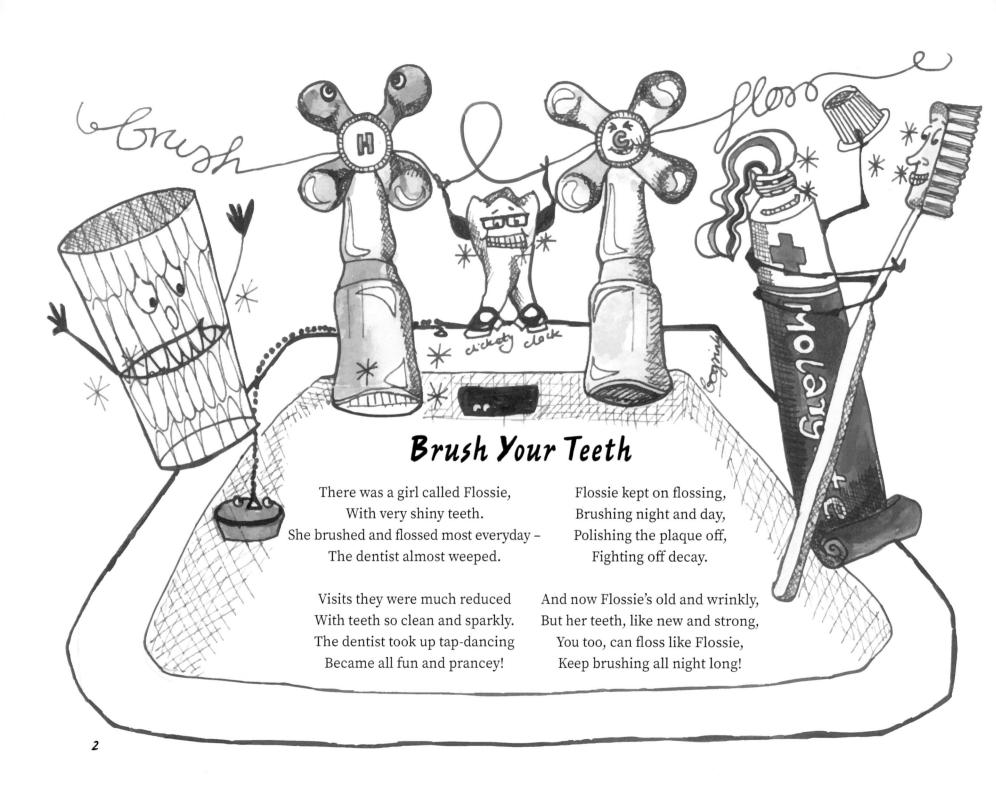

Brush Your Teeth

There was a girl called Flossie,
With very shiny teeth.
She brushed and flossed most everyday –
The dentist almost weeped.

Visits they were much reduced
With teeth so clean and sparkly.
The dentist took up tap-dancing
Became all fun and prancey!

Flossie kept on flossing,
Brushing night and day,
Polishing the plaque off,
Fighting off decay.

And now Flossie's old and wrinkly,
But her teeth, like new and strong,
You too, can floss like Flossie,
Keep brushing all night long!

The Dippy Eggs

"Do you like a dippy egg?"
Asked one egg to another.
"Oh yes I do –
Nice golden goo!"
Replying to his brother.

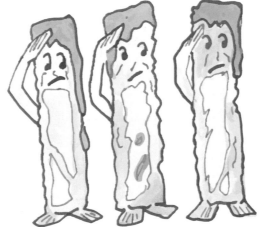

But little did he know his fate,
As the knife it sliced his head off.
But barely spoke,
As soldiers dove,
To mop up all his yolk.

"Oh brother, do not be alarmed!"
His eggy friend then cried.
"This is the better way to go,
Than scrambled, boiled or fried!"

3

Did You Ever Hear The Tale?

That kid who always cried for help. I quote:
"Last seen as a billy goat."
Constant bleating for attention,
Ears to horns, too small to mention.

Or that hag who worked out-flat
And turned into a tabby cat.
Her nag transformed into a purr,
Tough skin and bones, to soft cat fur.

Did you ever hear the tale?
Of the girl who turned into a snail?
Into deepest sleep she fell,
Her duvet wrapped into a shell.

The lad that never ate his greens
And became a field of beans?
His teeth turned all to seeds,
And his toenails full of weeds.

Or that lass who when she showered
Always lasted hours and hours?
Arms turned to fins, away she swam
Now salmon trying to jump a dam.

And that boy who gamed night and day?
Well he just quietly flew away.
Treecreeper, outdoors in the wild,
Nothing like that sickly child.

And did you hear a funny rumour —
That man, without a sense of humour?
His frown? Now a set of smiling chomps,
A hyena across desert, romps.

That big boy bully in the upper school,
Who picked on small kids, what a fool.
Last known as a wiggly worm,
A blackbird's dinner, all but confirmed.

In case you have not got it yet,
A small reminder, lest you forget:
Those that spend much time amusing,
Working, shouting, or abusing,
Will henceforth become their ani-vice,
(And really, this is not so nice):
Be that snake, or frog, or squirrel.
Ignore this warning at your peril.

5

How to Tie Laces?

How to tie laces
To win running races?
How to strap boots
To mount arduous routes?
How to bow shoes
To dance closely in twos?

Start with a loop,
Follow through with the string,
Then double-back through the new hole,
Pull through tight on the thing.

Or easier still is
Two bunny ears.
Knot them tightly together,
Like two little dears.

But Mum I am gone
'Cos my shoes are elastic!
And mine Mum, is Velcro,
And that is fantastic.

6

School Safari

Do you ever walk to school?
I do too, it's really cool.
Hand in hand as crocodile,
Get there with a snappy smile.

One day, you know, I missed the bus.
But tell me, please? Why all the fuss?
Stride out now and a quick march, boss!
But stop to let the zebra cross.

Next day, fearing to be late,
As an eagle to the gate.
All the short-cuts I did run,
Straight to school 'fore bell was rung!

I stick to path and paving slabs,
Avoiding all the little cracks.
Step on them, or stray too wide,
Lions and hogs will have my hide!

Cat Attack

Fat cat,
Slim cat,
Cuddle cat,
Jim cat.

Lost cat?
Found cat.
Small cat?
Round cat.

Cat stirs —
Cat purrs.
Cat sleeps,
Cat peeps.

Cat nights —
Cat fights.
Cat tails,
Cat wails.

Long cat,
Cool cat,
Box cat,
Pool cat.

Desk cat,
Zoom cat,
Keyboard cat,
Cat chat.

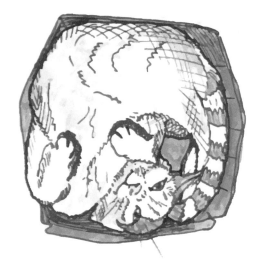

Cat fleas!
Cat sneeze,
Cat tease,
Cat freeze.

Cat kiss,
Cat lick,
Cat nap,
Cat nip.

Scratchy cat,
Strokey cat,
Scaredy cat,
Stretchy cat.

Family cat,
Stray cat,
Tom cat,
Play cat.

Cat bounce,
Cat pounce,
Cat stalk,
Cat walk.

Cat lives?
Cat survives.
Cat hides,
Cat thrives.

Cat on the table,
Cat in bed,
Cat on the chair,
Cat in my head.

Pumpkin Story

I had a little pumpkin seed,
No bigger than my toe.
I popped it in a little pot,
And then to watch it grow.

It sprouted two green angel wings.
That to the sky unfurled.
I watered roots, and all the shoots,
Raised heads, so bright and bold.

When the sun had warmed the earth,
And my little sprouts were strong,
I took them from the nursery bed,
To compost, leaves and dung.

But then the darkest hour had come,
With battle 'gainst the beasts.
Armed with beer, and salt, and scissors,
To thwart their midnight feasts.

A TINY SEED

PUMPKIN SEEDS

BEER IN HERE!

Busy
Buzzy
Bumble
Bee

Buzz

Buzz

Survivors counted on one hand,
Now race to catch the hours,
And burst, and thrust and tangle on,
With blooms of peachy flowers.

Humming soldiers striped in black,
Must stamp and spread their gold.
As blossom season shrivels up,
And tiny gourds unfold.

And oh, those fruits, my pumpkin love,
'Neath leaves and stalks do run.
Streaked of yellow, amber, rust,
Just like the setting sun.

My pumpkin promise grows and swells,
With rain and showers drenched.
Scorched beneath the summer heat,
And rambling through the fence.

Then come one late September day,
When ripe for carriage size,
Hollow-heavy, cut the trunk,
And claim the bounty prize!

Pumpkin parade a-top a barrow,
Then store them somewhere cool.
Until time comes to scoop the flesh,
Slice grins and teeth that drool.

Pumpkin praise with song and thanks
For a harvest that came good.
Then roast and spice my pumpkin up,
A pie, a soup, a pud?

And this the pumpkin story's end,
When freezing winds do blow
And down there, in the cellar deep,
My golden pumpkin glows.

ANOTHER
TINY
SEED

Ode to the Lonesome Sock

Igad, Igod, I am,
A lonesome sock,
And I fear —
My partner will
Never be near again,
For he is lost.
And I am destined to roam,
This world alone,

Or sometimes randomly
paired
And worn with another.
Then always referred,
A little absurd,
As 'odd socks.'
But Hey! I found a friend,
And that rocks!

THE PAIR GAME....

The Stair of Despair

A brush, or a book,
A belt or a knicker,
Put me away!
Nothing is quicker.

I want to go up,
And be put away,
But I don't have the legs,
So here I will stay.

This is the stair,
The stair of despair.
Please take a care,
And put me up there.

TO THE TOP!

KEEP GOING

UP

ONWARDS AND UPWARDS

TIDY UP!

PANT MAN

THE ONLY WAY IS UP

THIS IS THE STAIR OF DESPAIR

TIDY

Clothesline Haiku

Pegging out the clothes,
One by one to blow free
Fly in the sunshine.

Toast

We are making the most
Of our toast.
Out of bed and
Straight to the bread.
Good morning.

Some tea too,
For me.
Whilst you're up —
Mine in a teacup.
Please?

The toast, out it pops!
Catch it, it's hot!
I'll have a banana.
Crumbs what a drama.
Thank you.

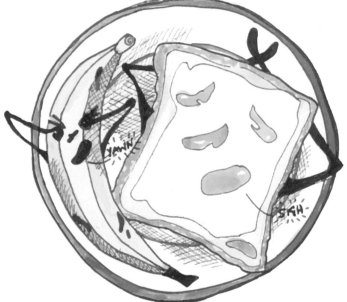

One or two slices?
That would be nice.
Can you take off the crusts?
In butter we trust.
Please?

Pass me a plate,
I'm going to be late.
I'd like the honey,
Why isn't it runny?
Please?

Silence.
We are making the most,
Of our toast.
It's too early to talk,
And we are trying to be polite.

There's a Dragon in the Fire

There's a dragon in the fire,
Here to drag you upwards: higher,
Dancing in a shower of stars,
That bounce and shoot from glowing hearth.

There's a village in the sticks,
With snaking paths that hook and twist,
And tiny, little nooks and crannies,
With shadows hung of ghosts and grannies.

There's a spell inside that smoke,
Filled with magic in its stroke.
Curling, drawn towards the moon,
Swirling to the midnight tune.

There are witches round the hearth,
Hear them as they cackle, laugh.
Old friends, old fruits, and old desires,
Bring folks of all sorts round the fires.

That be gold amongst the embers,
Glowing bright with glittering cinders.
Ash and fairy dust inside.
Cold to touch, the fire's died.

Bedtime Routine

Read us a book Dad!
Make it all bad
Of pirate adventures,
Who take no survivors!

Son, I start with a story:
Not very gory,
A cautionary tale,
Of slumber and ale.

Oh, Dad tell us a yarn,
That's as long as your arm.
Of Pinocchio's nose,
And a fib, how it grows.

Son, remember that time,
Where everything rhymed.
When wolves hid in roots,
And cats, they wore boots.

Dad, how did it end?
With a fight to defend?
With a massive great battle?
And a final death rattle?

Son, it was rather a feast,
And a beautiful beast.
Then later a wish,
Then a spell, and a hush.

Dad, are you awake?
Or is too late?
Are they together forever?
Or just in good weather?

Son, again and once more
Dad's asleep on the floor.
Please get some rest too.
Lights out, sleep tight, you.

Mum, tell us a dream
Of rain and sunbeams.
Of white racing horses
And magical forces.

Son, give it a rest!
We're doing our best.
This, the last warning,
Lights out, till the morning!

Tickled Pink

Never forget the skin that you're in.
From the hair on your head to the heel of your shin.

Spin around till the world goes giddy.
Get tickled pink at something silly.
Laugh so hard till both sides ache.
Hiccups from a shock you take.

To roll or not to roll your tongue?
To suck or not to suck your thumb?
A statue, pins and needles stuck.
Tears of salt when things just suck.

Run till you are all out of puff.
Hand wrestle mates of stronger stuff.
Burn with a blush from something sweet.
Soak in the tub, till wrinkled feet.

Throwback your chin with mighty mane,
Sneeze out loud like a hurricane.
Pardon me, with my bottom burp.
Bleed red blood when I get hurt.

It's not the shade that counts, or the place you're from,
But being human, everyone.

Lightning Source UK Ltd.
Milton Keynes UK
UKRC032336160222
398779UK00001B/13